The Best
Arsenal
Trivia Book Ever

300+ Interesting Trivia Questions and Random,
Shocking, Fun Facts Every Gunners Fan Needs to Know

House of Ballers

YOUR FREE BONUS!

- What did Materazzi say to earn a headbutt from Zidane on the biggest stage of them all?
- Who got shot for scoring an own goal at the World Cup?
- What did Maradona reveal on his autobiography about the 'Hand of God'?

Find out by scanning the QR Code below with your smartphone:

Contents

INTRODUCTION

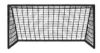

In a sport where trophies are the barometer of success, the history, success, and fame of Arsenal FC simply cannot go unnoticed. In the committee of super clubs, superstar footballers and gaffers, Arsenal FC stands tall as both a sporting institution and a financial behemoth.

A huge social media followership of above 70m individuals pays homage to the worldwide brand that Arsenal has evolved to become. From its humble beginnings as a club founded by munitions workers at the Royal Arsenal, the club is now worth $2.8 billion according to Forbes and pulls in close to half-a-billion in revenue every year. That figure makes the club the fifth largest in England and the eighth largest in the world.

Initially named Dial Square by its founders led by David Danskin, Arsenal went through a series of home grounds in its early years – Plumstead Common, Manor Ground, and Invicta Ground quickly gave way to Highbury in 1913 before the ultramodern £390 million Emirates Stadium became the Gunners' new stomping ground in 2006.

In 136 years of existence, there has never been a dearth of drama, great footballers or exciting football on show, but the first great figure appeared in 1925 in Herbert Chapman. After suffering relegation in 1913, Arsenal had gradually grown in strength and size, and Chapman's arrival in 1925 finally blew Arsenal onto the big stage. After a rebuild project that took five years, the 1930s finally opened the first era of dominance. 5 League Championships and 2 FA cups in the 1930s announced the arrival of Arsenal as a perennial force in English football. Not even Chapman's tragic death in 1934 from pneumonia could throw a spanner in the wheels he had set in motion.

Further success arrived after the World War – a league title in 1947/48, a third

FA cup in 1950 and a record-breaking seventh league in 1952/53 painted a picture of true dominance for the club in North London. However, Arsenal had lost more players to the war than any other club.

Coupled with crippling debt, the Gunners went on a decline until they won their first European honours with the 1969/70 Inter-Cities Fairs Cup, followed by the first League and FA Cup double in the next season. The success was not sustained though and a lean period set in until the decade-long era of George Graham in 1986 and the emergence of "the Famous Back Four" put Arsenal back on the map. Several league titles and cup successes restored Arsenal's claim to dominance and until Graham was ignominiously dismissed.

The arrival of the little-known Arsene Wenger in 1996 however completely changed the club's philosophy and league football in England. An influx of French talent including the meteoric Henry, Vieira, Pires and Emmanuel Petit spurred the Gunners onto their best era and a fierce rivalry with Manchester United. In the first nine seasons of the Wenger era, Arsenal only finished below second once.

Two League and FA Cup doubles and three PL titles tell only a fraction of the exciting times and in the 2003/04 season, Wenger's team finally overdid itself by going the whole season unbeaten while playing very attractive football. While the Gunners have not reached the same heights since then, the sight of the famous Red and White jersey instantly evokes sensations bordering on frenzy and terrific excitement among fans and even opponents.

The goals have never dried up, the team has always been filled with great personalities and records seem to be made every season. The heroics of David Seaman and Mad Jens thrilled the fans year after year, and in front of the goalkeepers, the defensive solidity of Tony Adams, David O'Leary and Nigel Winterburn was the stuff of legends. Patrick Vieira, Gilberto Silva and Emmanuel Petit are only some of the names of midfielders who have brought power and technique to the engine room.

And in front of them, forwards from across the world have left the fans on the edge of their seat. From the cold-bloodedness of Thiery Henry to the reliable Ian Wright; from the gangly Nwankwo Kanu to the sweet volleys from Robin van Persie, Arsenal fans have been treated to spectacle after spectacle. What Herbert Chapman started has grown in leaps and bounds under names like George Graham and Arsene Wenger.

Yes, we can go on talking about Arsenal FC, but how much do you really know about the Gunners from North London? Who threw a pizza at Sir Alex Ferguson in the famous Pizzagate scandal? Which oft-forgotten player is the youngest permanent captain in Arsenal's history? Which captain sat down and cried after a draw with Birmingham FC?

If you will like the answers to these and many more questions, then this is the book for you.

Are you an ardent football lover like me? Are you an Arsenal fan who thinks he knows everything about the club? Are you willing to test your knowledge of Arsenal FC's history? Do you simply want to know more about the red side of North London?

If you have answered 'yes' to any of these questions, then, this book is certainly for YOU!

Compiled for every football lover, especially diehard Arsenal fans, this book is divided into 12 fun-filled chapters. Each chapter holds 20 entertaining and informative trivia questions and their answers, and 10 fun-filled facts. Every chapter will leave you lusting for more facts about one of the biggest sporting institutions in the world.

At the end of this book, you will be armed with enough facts to blow other fans and even rivals out of the water when it comes to Arsenal FC. We will touch every topic including the club's origin, stadia, trophies, records, biggest transfer deals and biggest matches. From a non-flying Dutchman, and a match-fixing scandal, from an unbeaten season to dominating the FA cups, Arsenal FC are never far away from the news.

Are you ready to be left on the edge of your seat?

Well then, Come On, You Gunner!

ORIGIN

"With a great name like ours, only success is good enough."

- Liam Brady

20 Trivia Questions

1. When was the first season Arsenal featured in the first division?

    A. 1893

    B. 1913

    C. 1904

    D. 1899

2. When was the first and only year Arsenal was relegated?

    A. 1912

    B. 1913

    C. 1914

    D. 1915

3. In what year was Arsenal founded?

    A. 1881

    B. 1886

    C. 1891

    D. 1896

4. Which of these is Arsenal's most famous nickname?

    A. The Reds

    B. The Arsenal

    C. The Cannons

    D. The Gunners

5. Who was Arsenal's first-ever captain?

    A. Morris Bates

    B. William Stewart

    C. David Danskin

    D. Arthur Brown

6. In what year was the current Arsenal crest introduced?

    A. 2004

    B. 2002

    C. 2000

    D. 1998

7. In what year did Arsenal join the English Football League as Woolwich Arsenal?

    A. 1893

    B. 1897

    C. 1887

    D. 1889

8. What was the name of Arsenal FC when it was founded?

    A. Royal Arsenal

    B. Woolwich Arsenal

    C. Dial Square

    D. The Arsenal

9. Which team did Arsenal play against in their first Premier League match?

    A. Newcastle

    B. Middlesbrough

    C. Fulham

    D. Norwich City

10. In what year was the first Arsenal crest unveiled?

    A. 1883

    B. 1888

    C. 1892

    D. 1898

11. How much did each of the 15 munition workers in Woolwich contribute to form the club?

    A. Six pence

    B. Nine pence

    C. Twelve pence

    D. Fifteen pence

12. What is the motto of Arsenal FC?

    A. Nil Satis nisi optimum (Nothing but the best is good enough)

    B. Mes Que un club (More than a club)

    C. Consectatio Excellentiae (In pursuit of excellence)

    D. Victoria Concordia Crescit (Victory through harmony)

13. What was the nationality of Arsenal FC's first-ever captain?

    A. Swiss

    B. Irish

    C. English

    D. Scottish

14. In 1919, Arsenal was controversially elected into the first division at the expense of which club?

    A. Chelsea

    B. Tottenham Hotspur

    C. Liverpool

    D. Fulham

15. The club's official mascot is a representation of which animal?

    A. Lion

    B. Bull

    C. Dinosaur

    D. Elephant

16. The first English League match to be broadcast live on radio in 1927 was between Arsenal and which Club?

    A. Sheffield United

    B. Liverpool

    C. Sheffield Wednesday

    D. Manchester United

17. What was the first competitive honour won by the club?

    A. League Cup

    B. FA Cup

    C. First Division title

    D. FA Charity Shield (FA Community Shield)

18. What year did Arsenal win their first European trophy?

    A. 1973

    B. 1972

    C. 1971

    D. 1970

19. Who contributed an additional three shillings to help form the club?

    A. Henry Norris

    B. David Danskin

    C. Leslie Knighton

    D. Morris Bates

20. Who was Arsenal's first-ever permanent manager?

    A.   Thomas Mitchell

    B.   William Elcoat

    C.   Harry Bradshaw

    D.   Leslie Knighton

20 Trivia Answers

1. C – 1904

2. B – 1913

3. B – 1886

4. D – The Gunners

5. C – David Danskin

6. B – 2002

7. A – 1893

8. C – Dial Square

9. D – Norwich City

10. B – 1888

11. A – Six Pence

12. D – Victoria Concordia Crescit (Victory Through Harmony)

13. D – Scotland

14. B – Tottenham Hotspur

15. C – Dinosaur

16. A – Sheffield United

17. B – FA Cup

18. D – 1970

19. B – David Danskin

20. A – Thomas Mitchell

10 Fun Facts

1. Several workers from the Woolwich Arsenal Armament Factory founded the club known presently as Arsenal FC in late 1886. The name at conception was Dial Square, in reference to the sundial at the top of the entrance to the factory.

2. Following a 6-0 triumph over Eastern Wanderers in their first-ever game on December 11, 1886, the name 'Royal Arsenal' was adopted to replace 'Dial Square'. The new name came from a combination of the Royal Oak Pub, where the founders' meeting took place, and the founders' workplace, the Arsenal armament factory, in Woolwich.

3. The famous red home colours of the club were adopted when a group of players newly recruited from Nottingham Forest asked their former club for a spare kit. Arsenal stuck with the borrowed colours.

4. Royal Arsenal first appeared in the FA Cup in the 1889/90 season. The club recorded notable successes that season, winning the London Charity Cup, The Kent Senior Cup and the Kent Junior Cup.

5. Royal Arsenal began to maintain increased professionalism due to increased playing success. This annoyed certain football authorities leading to their expulsion from the London FA Cup and a subsequent boycott by several Southern amateur clubs. The club's name was changed to Woolwich Arsenal during the off-season of 1893.

6. The club was invited to join the Football League in 1893, two years after turning professional. The club had earlier sought to establish a Southern equivalent of the Football League, but the move did not materialize.

7. Arsenal first gained promotion to the top flight, what was then known as Division One, in 1903. They also reached back-to-back FA Cup semifinals three years later

8. Following relegation from the top tier and a move into the club's new ground at Highbury in 1913 under the chairmanship of Henry Norris, Woolwich was dropped from the club's name. Norris became Arsenal chairman while still holding a similar role at Fulham. The club has since then been known as Arsenal football club.

9. Henry Norris once sought to merge Arsenal and Fulham, but the English Football League shot the idea down. Due to a potential conflict of interest, Norris stepped down at Fulham to concentrate on Arsenal.

10. After playing for two seasons without a logo, Arsenal adopted an emblem in 1988 that features a cannon symbolic of the club's foundations. The current badge is a single golden cannon facing eastward.

STADIUM

"I always wanted to play in English football, and Arsenal and Highbury is English football to me."

- Dennis Bergkamp

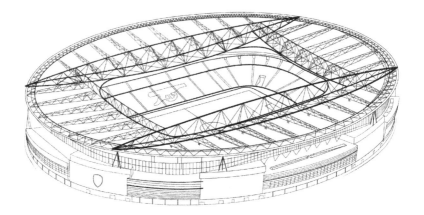

20 Trivia Questions

1. What was the nickname for Arsenal former stadium, Highbury?

    A. Home of Football

    B. Stadium of Football

    C. Home of the Gunners

    D. Stadium of the Gunners

2. Which club did Arsenal face in the first competitive match at Emirates stadium?

    A. Ajax

    B. Portsmouth

    C. Aston Villa

    D. Benfica

3. What was the dimension of the football pitch at Highbury Stadium?

    A. 106 x 76 yards

    B. 109 x 73 yards

    C. 109 x 70 yards

    D. 106 x 73 yards

4. Who was the first Arsenal player to receive a red card at the Emirates Stadium?

    A. Philippe Senderos

    B. Gilberto Silva

    C. Lauren

    D. Mathieu Flamini

5. Who was the architect that originally designed the Highbury Stadium?

    A. Edwin Lutyens

    B. Archibald Leitch

    C. Herbert Baker

    D. Populous

6. In what year did Arsenal move to Highbury?

    A. 1911

    B. 1912

    C. 1913

    D. 1914

7. Where is the Emirates stadium located?

    A. Holloway

    B. Harringay

    C. Canonbury

    D. Barnsbury

8. Against which club did Arsenal record the lowest attendance at Highbury in a League match?

    A. Leeds United

    B. Norwich City

    C. Barnsley

    D. Nottingham Forest

9. What is the pitch size at the Emirates stadium?

    A. 111.8 x 74.1 yards

    B. 112.8 x 74.4 yards

    C. 113.8 x 74.1 yards

    D. 114.8 x 74.4 yards

10. What was the estimated construction cost of Arsenal's current home ground?

    A. £350 million

    B. £390 million

    C. £450 million

    D. £590 million

11. Who was the first player to be sent off at the Emirates stadium?

    A. Philippe Senderos

    B. Sol Campbell

    C. Ivan Campo

    D. Rio Ferdinand

12. Which stand at the Emirates stadium was formerly known as the Laundry End?

    A. North Bank Stand

    B. South Stand

    C. East Stand

    D. West Stand

13. Which of these stadia did Arsenal never use as a home ground?

    A. Field Mill

    B. Invicta Ground

    C. Manor Ground

    D. Wembley Stadium

14. What is the seating capacity of the Emirates stadium?

    A. 50,260

    B. 55,260

    C. 60,260

    D. 65,260

15. Which architectural firm designed The Emirates Stadium?

    A. HMC Architects

    B. Populous

    C. Jacobs

    D. LMN Architects

16. Who was the first player to score a goal in a competitive match at the Emirates stadium?

    A. Gabriel Agbonlahor

    B. Gareth Barry

    C. John Carew

    D. Olof Mellberg

17. Who was the first Arsenal player to score a goal in a competitive match at the Emirates stadium?

    A. Thierry Henry

    B. Dennis Bergkamp

    C. Gilberto Silva

    D. Emmanuel Adebayor

18. Which stand in the Emirates stadium is popularly known as the Clock End?

    A. North Bank

    B. East Stand

    C. South Stand

    D. West Stand

19. What was Arsenal's biggest winning margin at the Highbury?

    A. 13:0

    B. 11:0

    C. 11:1

    D. 13:1

20. Who was Arsenal's opponent at the match with the highest-ever attendance at the Emirates stadium?

    A. Manchester United

    B. Tottenham Hotspur

    C. Chelsea

    D. Liverpool

20 Trivia Answers

1. A – Home of Football

2. C – Aston Villa

3. B – 109 x 73 yards

4. A – Philippe Senderos

5. B – Archibald Leitch

6. C – 1913

7. A – Holloway

8. A – Leeds United

9. D – 114.8 x 74.4 yards

10. B - £390 million

11. C – Ivan Campo

12. A – North Bank Stand

13. A – Field Mill

14. C – 60,250

15. B – Populous

16. D – Olof Mellberg

17. C – Gilberto Silva

18. C – South Stand

19. C – 11:1

20. A –Manchester United

10 Fun Facts

1.   In their formative years, Arsenal floated between a number of different grounds in the Plumstead area. Royal Arsenal secured the lease of Sportsman Ground on Plumstead Marshes, having used Plumstead Common in their maiden season. They soon moved into the Manor Ground due to increased following and support.

2.   The club moved to the Invicta Ground in 1891. They stayed there for nearly six years until a rent increase prompted a move back to their old Manor Ground home, which they bought immediately. They stayed on Manor Ground until their move to Highbury in 1913.

3.   The last game Arsenal played at its old Manor Ground home was a 1-1 draw against Middlesbrough on April 26, 1913, and the first at Highbury was a 2-1 victory against Leicester Fosse.

4.   The Arsenal stadium at Highbury was designed by Archibald Leitch, renowned for also designing stands for clubs like Manchester United, Chelsea, Everton, Tottenham, and Glasgow Rangers. The main stand resided on the East side with a capacity of 9,000 spectators.

5.   The club paid a further sum of £64,000 in 1925 to secure complete ownership of the Highbury stadium site. Restrictions such as not playing on Christmas Day and Good Friday were then removed.

6.   Architect Claude Waterloo Ferrier designed the West Stand at the Club's Highbury home, and it came into use in 1932. It had seats for 4,000 spectators and a standing capacity of 17,000.

7.   The stadium name was changed to Arsenal stadium in the 1930s. In October 1936, the art deco style East Stand listed then as Grade Two was commissioned. It housed offices, players' facilities, and the main entrance (Marble Halls).

8. Arsenal stadium was used as a first-aid post during the Second World War. Incendiary bombs destroyed the North Bank roof during the war. It was rebuilt in 1956. Floodlights were introduced in 1951, followed by undersoil heating in 1964.

9. The 2005/06 season was Arsenal's last at Highbury. The club wore red-current tops as a tribute to the first Arsenal teams to play on that ground. In the last game at Highbury, Arsenal beat Wigan Athletic 4-2 thanks to a Thierry Henry hat-trick to secure UEFA Champions League qualification on May 7, 2006.

10. Since the start of 2006/07, Arsenal have played their home games at the new Emirates stadium ground. It is situated on Ashburton Grove in the North London borough of Islington. Its capacity of 60,355 makes it the fourth largest in England, behind Wembley, Old Trafford, and more recently, the Tottenham Hotspur stadium.

MANAGERS

"I think we can go a whole season unbeaten."

- Arsene Wenger

20 Trivia Questions

1. Who is Arsenal's longest-serving manager?

    A. Herbert Chapman

    B. Arsene Wenger

    C. George Graham

    D. Bertie Mee

2. Who was Arsenal's first professional manager?

    A. William Elcoat

    B. Phil Kelso

    C. George Morrell

    D. Thomas Mitchell

3. Which manager led Arsenal to win the FA Cup in 1930?

    A. George Graham

    B. Tom Whittaker

    C. Herbert Chapman

    D. Jack Clayton

4. Which of these managers won the European Cup Winners' Cup with the club?

    A. George Graham

    B. Arsene Wenger

    C. Unai Emery

    D. Terry Neill

5. Which of these Arsenal managers won the most FA Cups for the club?

    A. Arsene Wenger

    B. George Graham

    C. Herbert Chapman

    D. Bertie Mee

6. Who is Arsenal's second longest-serving manager?

    A. Terry Neill

    B. Bertie Mee

    C. Tom Whittaker

    D. George Allison

7. Which of these managers replaced George Graham in 1995?

    A. Arsene Wenger

    B. Bruce Rioch

    C. Don Howe

    D. Billy Wright

8. What is the nationality of former Arsenal head coach Unai Emery?

   A. Danish

   B. Swedish

   C. French

   D. Spanish

9. Which of these managers has a statue outside the Emirates stadium?

   A. Herbert Chapman

   B. Bertie Mee

   C. George Graham

   D. Terry Neill

10. Which of these managers served in 2 different spells as a caretaker manager?

   A. Tom Whittaker

   B. Stewart Houston

   C. William Elcoat

   D. Harry Bradshaw

11. Who was Arsenal's Manager when professional football resumed in 1919?

   A. James McEwen

   B. Herbert Chapman

   C. Leslie Knighton

   D. Billy Wright

12. Which permanent manager replaced Herbert Chapman after his unfortunate demise?

    A. George Allison

    B. Tom Whittaker

    C. Jack Clayton

    D. George Swindin

13. Which of these Arsenal managers was formerly the club's physiotherapist?

    A. George Swindin

    B. Terry Neill

    C. Steve Burtenshaw

    D. Burtie Mee

14. Which one of these managers was not a caretaker manager?

    A. James McEwen

    B. Joe Shaw

    C. Bruce Rioch

    D. Pat Rice

15. In what year was Arsene Wenger appointed as Arsenal manager?

    A. 1995

    B. 1996

    C. 1997

    D. 1998

16. Who was the first Arsenal manager from Scotland?

    A. George Graham

    B. George Morrell

    C. Thomas Mitchell

    D. Phil Kelso

17. Which of these managers did not win an FA Cup for the club?

    A. Unai Emery

    B. Mikel Arteta

    C. George Graham

    D. Terry Neill

18. Who was the caretaker manager when Unai Emery left the club?

    A. Mikel Arteta

    B. Dennis Bergkamp

    C. Per Mertesacker

    D. Freddie Ljungberg

19. Who was the first non-English manager of Arsenal FC?

    A. Unai Emery

    B. Steve Burtenshaw

    C. Arsene Wenger

    D. Phil Kelso

20. Which of these managers was the first to win a 'double' for Arsenal?

    A.   Bertie Mee

    B.   Arsene Wenger

    C.   George Graham

    D.   George Swindin

20 Trivia Answers

1. B – Arsene Wenger

2. D – Thomas Mitchell

3. C – Herbert Chapman

4. A – George Graham

5. A – Arsene Wenger

6. D – George Allison

7. B – Bruce Rioch

8. D – Spain

9. A – Herbert Chapman

10. B – Stewart Houston

11. C – Leslie Knighton

12. A – George Allison

13. D – Burtie Mee

14. C – Bruce Rioch

15. B – 1996

16. C – Thomas Mitchell

17. A – Unai Emery

18. D – Freddie Ljungberg

19. C – Arsene Wenger

20. A – Bertie Mee

10 Fun Facts

1. Sam Hollis was the first person to take charge of team affairs when he was appointed secretary-manager in 1894. The team had been managed by a committee of players and club members before his appointment. He kept the club at midtable in the Second Division during his three years at the club before he left for Bristol City in 1897.

2. Thomas Brown Mitchell was the first professional manager in Arsenal history when he joined the club in 1897. The Scotsman had been the secretary at Blackburn Rovers for twelve years before his appointment. He led Arsenal past the FA Cup qualifying rounds and fifth in the Second Division before resigning in March 1898.

3. Harry Bradshaw is regarded as Arsenal's first successful manager, having led the club to promotion to the First Division in 1904 and a top-three finish in the league in 1902/1903. He moved on to Fulham in May 1904 and was later appointed secretary of the Southern League.

4. Scotsman Phil Kelso was the first to manage Arsenal in the English top tier, having inherited the job from promotion-winning manager Harry Bradshaw in 1904. He led the club to consecutive FA Cup semifinals before leaving in 1908.

5. Woolwich Arsenal made a move from Plumstead in southeast London to Highbury in North London under the tutelage of George Morrell. He took over in 1908 and finished sixth in his first season despite being forced to sell a number of his best players. The club suffered its sole relegation from the top flight during his reign, finishing bottom in 1913.

6. Leslie Knighton was the first Arsenal manager appointed after the club had been re-elected into the First Division following World War I. He took charge of 268 games from 1919 to 1925 before being dismissed after finishing 20th in

1924/1925.

7. Englishman, Herbert Chapman, took charge of the Gunners 403 times and during that time established the club as a force to be reckoned with in English football. He had been manager at Leeds City and Huddersfield Town before being appointed Arsenal manager. Chapman led the club to its first FA Cup and First Division titles in 1930 and 1931. He led the club to another title in 1933, before his sudden demise in 1934 at the age of 55.

8. George Allison became Arsenal manager in June 1934 following the tragic passing away of legendary manager Herbert Chapman. Allison had previously been programme editor, secretary, and managing director at the club. He guided the club to a third successive league title in 1935 and the FA Cup in 1936. The then Arsenal manager won another league title in 1938 before retiring from the game in 1947.

9. Bertie Mee led Arsenal to its first League and FA cup double in 1971. He was appointed as a manager in 1966, and he recruited Dave Sexton and Don Howe as part of his backroom staff. Under his tutelage, the club finished runners-up in the League Cup in 1968 and 1969. He guided the club to its first piece of silverware in 17 years with a 4-3 aggregate win against Anderlecht in the Inter-Cities Fairs Cup final in 1970.

10. Considered by many as the club's second most successful manager, former Arsenal player George Graham rejoined the club in 1986. He went on to win two League titles, two League cups, one FA Cup, and the UEFA Cup Winners Cup during eight years.

GOALIES

"Goalkeeping is like extreme sports sometimes – you have to let yourself go."

- Jens Lehmann

20 Trivia Questions

1. Which of these goalies has the highest number of appearances for Arsenal FC?

    A. David Seaman

    B. Jens Lehman

    C. Petr Cech

    D. Manuel Almunia

2. From which club did Jens Lehmann join Arsenal F.C?

    A. Stuttgart

    B. Bayern Munich

    C. Borussia Dortmund

    D. Borussia Monchengladbach

3. Which of these Arsenal goalies saved Paul Scholes' penalty in the 2005 FA Cup final?

    A. Manuel Almunia

    B. Jens Lehmann

    C. Stuart Taylor

    D. Vito Mannone

4. Which of these goalies was between the sticks when the club won the 2020 FA Cup?

    A. Bernd Leno

    B. David Ospina

    C. Petr Cech

    D. Emiliano Martinez

5. Which of these Arsenal goalies won the Premier League Golden Glove award?

    A. Jens Lehmann

    B. Wojciech Szczesny

    C. David Seaman

    D. Bernd Leno

6. Which of these goalies was between the sticks when the club won the 2017 FA Cup?

    A. Petr Cech

    B. Emiliano Martinez

    C. Bernd Leno

    D. David Ospina

7. What is the nationality of former Arsenal shot-stopper Lukasz Fabianski?

    A. Serbian

    B. Croat

    C. Polish

    D. Albanian

8. How many consecutive clean sheets did Jens Lehmann keep in the 2005/06 Champions League campaign?

    A. 8

    B. 6

    C. 4

    D. 2

9. From which club was Aaron Ramsdale signed from?

    A. Brighton & Hove Albion F.C

    B. AFC Bournemouth

    C. Sheffield United

    D. Fulham F.C.

10. Where was Bernd Leno signed from?

    A. Bayer Leverkusen

    B. Vfb Stuttgart

    C. Werder Bremen

    D. Borussia Dortmund

11. How many Premier League appearances did John Lukic manage in his second stint with Arsenal?

    A. 24

    B. 21

    C. 18

    D. 15

12. Former Arsenal goalie, Vito Mannone, hails from which country?

    A. Spain

    B. Italy

    C. Netherlands

    D. France

13. How many FA Cups did David Seaman win with Arsenal?

    A. 6

    B. 5

    C. 4

    D. 3

14. Which of these goalies scored a league goal for the club?

    A. Frank Moss

    B. David Seaman

    C. George Swindin

    D. Bob Wilson

15. What was Jens Lehmann's nickname?

    A. Savior Jens

    B. Great Jens

    C. Brick Jens

    D. Mad Jens

What is the nationality of former Arsenal goalie Alfred Jack Kelsey?

A. English

B. Irish

C. Welsh

D. Scottish

16. Which of these goalies did Arsenal sign from their arch-rivals Tottenham?

A. Pat Jennings

B. David Seaman

C. George Swindin

D. John Lukic

17. Which Arsenal goalkeeper holds the record for most clean sheets for the club?

A. Jens Lehmann

B. Petr Cech

C. John Lukic

D. David Seaman

18. How many Premier League appearances did Vince Bartram manage for the club?

A. 15

B. 11

C. 9

D. 7

19. Which one of these Arsenal goalies spent only 12 months with the club?

    A. Richard Wright

    B. Vito Mannone

    C. Stuart Taylor

    D. Alex Manninger

20 Trivia Answers

1. A – David Seaman

2. C – Borussia Dortmund

3. B – Jens Lehmann

4. D – Emiliano Martinez

5. B – Wojciech Szczesny

6. D – David Ospina

7. C – Poland

8. A – 8

9. C – Sheffield United

10. A – Bayer Leverkusen

11. C – 18

12. B – Italy

13. C – 4

14. A – Frank Moss

15. D – Mad Jens

16. C – Wales

17. A – Pat Jennings

18. D – David Seaman

19. B – 11

20. A – Richard Wright

10 Fun Facts

1. David Danskin is the first goalkeeper in Arsenal history, joining the club in its first year from Nottingham Forest. Thanks to him and a few other Nottingham Forest players joining Arsenal that year, the club got its initial dark red colors.

2. Arsenal signed English goalkeeper, Frank Moss, from Oldham Athletic for £3,000 in November 1931. He made the first of his 143 appearances the following day at Chelsea. He enjoyed a relatively successful stay at the club, winning three league titles and the Charity Shield a couple of times. He even scored a league goal while at the club.

3. For much of the 2003/04 season, Jens Lehmann was in goal when Arsenal romped to a third Premier League crown without suffering a single defeat. He had joined the club in the summer of 2003 from Borussia Dortmund. He won the FA Cup in 2005 and helped Arsenal reach their first UEFA Champions League final in 2006. However, he was giving the marching orders in the showpiece as Arsenal lost 2-1 to FC Barcelona.

4. Welshman, Jack Kelsey, got his big break in 1952 following an injury to then Arsenal number one, George Swindin. He made 29 appearances as Arsenal won the league title that season. Jack would go on to outrightly claim the number one position for himself a year later. He represented Wales at its first World Cup appearance in 1958.

5. In an international career that lasted 22 years, Pat Jennings made a record 119 appearances for Northern Ireland. He spent eight years at Arsenal, having spent 13 years at Tottenham Hotspur. He helped Arsenal to the first League and FA Cup double, and he is considered one of the best ever players in his position.

6. David Seaman is arguably the best Arsenal goalkeeper of all time. The Englishman made a remarkable 564 appearances in the colors of Arsenal and won nine major trophies, including league and FA Cup doubles in 1998 and 2002. He helped Arsenal claim the 1994 UEFA Cup Winners Cup and captained the Gunners to

FA Cup victory in his last game in 2003.

7. John Lukic joined Arsenal for £75,000 in July 1983 as a long-term replacement for the legendary Pat Jennings. He became the club's first-choice shot-stopper at the halfway stage of the 1984/85 season. He helped the club win the League Cup in 1987 and the First Division title in 1989.

8. Having joined from London rivals Chelsea for 10m pounds in the summer of 2015, Petr Cech became the first keeper to win the Premier League Golden Glove with two different clubs in the 2015/16 Premier League season. He helped Arsenal to a 13th FA Cup in 2017 before retiring in 2019 with a record 202 Premier League clean sheets.

9. Arsenal was helped to the First Division for the first time thanks to James Ashcroft's commanding display in goal during the 1903/04 season. He kept 20 clean sheets and conceded just 22 goals in 34 games as the Gunners reached the top tier for the first time in their history. The club also reached two consecutive FA Cup semifinals during his eight-year stay that ended in 1908.

10. Goalkeeper Bob Wilson won the Player of the Year award as Arsenal won a historic first league and FA Cup double in 1971. He had helped the club clinch the Inter-Cities Fairs Cup a year earlier following his return from a hand injury sustained in the 1968/69 campaign. He was appointed goalkeeper trainer following his retirement and oversaw the developments of Jennings, Lukic, and Seaman.

DEFENDERS

"I will sign every contract Arsenal put in front of me without reading it."

- Tony Adams

20 Trivia Questions

1. How many Premier League title(s) did Ashley Cole win with Arsenal?

    A. 1

    B. 2

    C. 3

    D. 4

2. What was Tony Adams' preferred position?

    A. Left Back

    B. Right Back

    C. Centre Back

    D. Wing Back

3. Which of these defenders won the European Cup Winners' Cup with the club?

    A. Martin Keown

    B. Nigel Winterburn

    C. Pat Rice

    D. Sol Campbell

4. How many FA Cup(s) did Tony Adams win with the club?

    A. 4

    B. 3

    C. 2

    D. 1

5. What was Lee Dixon's preferred position?

    A. Wing Back

    B. Right Back

    C. Left Back

    D. Centre Back

6. Which defender received Arsenal's 100th Premier League red card?

    A. David Luiz

    B. Rob Holding

    C. Gabriel Magalhaes

    D. Calum Chambers

7. Which of these defenders was not part of 'The Invincibles'?

    A. Martin Keown

    B. Kolo Toure

    C. Pascal Cygan

    D. Tony Adams

8. What is the nationality of former Arsenal left-back Gael Clichy?

    A. French

    B. English

    C. Spanish

    D. Italian

9. Which defender holds the record for the most league appearances for Arsenal?

    A. Pat Rice

    B. Nigel Winterburn

    C. David O'Leary

    D. Lee Dixon

10. Which of these defenders has a statue at the Emirates Stadium?

    A. Nigel Winterburn

    B. Tony Adams

    C. Lee Dixon

    D. Martin Keown

11. From where was Thomas Vermaelen signed?

    A. Ajax F.C.

    B. Club Brugge

    C. Anderlecht

    D. Feyenoord

12. Which of these defenders did not win a trophy with the club?

    A. Bacary Sagna

    B. Per Mertesacker

    C. Kieran Gibbs

    D. Johan Djourou

13. How many League Cup(s) did David O'Leary win with the club?

    A. 4

    B. 3

    C. 2

    D. 1

14. Which of these defenders was nicknamed 'Mr. Arsenal'?

    A. Tony Adams

    B. Martin Keown

    C. David O'Leary

    D. Sol Campbell

15. Which of these defenders did not make more than 500 appearances for the club?

    A. Lee Dixon

    B. Nigel Winterburn

    C. Pat Rice

    D. Martin Keown

16. What is the nationality of Arsenal defender Pablo Mari?

    A. Brazilian

    B. Italian

    C. Spanish

    D. Ecuadorian

17. Which of these defenders was not part of the 'famous four' Arsenal backline?

    A. Steve Bould

    B. Martin Keown

    C. Tony Adams

    D. Lee Dixon

18. From which club was Lee Dixon signed?

    A. Birmingham City

    B. Chester City

    C. Stoke City

    D. Manchester City

19. Which of these Arsenal defenders was not among the 2019/20 FA Cup-winning squad?

    A. David Luiz

    B. Callum Chambers

    C. Cedric Soares

    D. Laurent Koscielny

20. Who holds the title for most red cards among Arsenal defenders in the Premier League?

   A. Martin Keown

   B. Laurent Koscielny

   C. Tony Adams

   D. David Luiz

20 Trivia Answers

1. B – 2

2. C – Centre Back

3. B – Nigel Winterburn

4. B – 3

5. B – Right Back

6. C – Gabriel Magalhaes

7. D – Tony Adams

8. A – France

9. C – David O'Leary

10. B – Tony Adams

11. A – Ajax

12. D – Johan Djourou

13. C – 2

14. A – Tony Adams

15. D – Martin Keown

16. C – Spanish

17. B – Martin Keown

18. C – Stoke City

19. D – Laurent Koscielny

20. A -Martin Keown

10 Fun Facts

1. Tony Adams held the Arsenal captaincy for 14 years and made 669 appearances for the club while picking up ten major honours along the way. He was the quintessential one-club player, rightfully nicknamed 'Mr. Arsenal' and unarguably one of the best to play for the North London club. He formed a solid partnership with Steve Bould at the heart of the Gunners defense and led the club to championship titles in three different decades.

2. Arsenal's record appearance holder, David O'Leary, turned out 722 times for the North London outfit. He joined the club in 1973 and became a regular from 1975 to his departure in 1993. He carried down the dogged mentality of the Arsenal sides of the 70s to their more successful counterparts of the late 80s and early 90s. During his stellar 19 seasons at Highbury, he helped the club claim two league titles, two FA Cups, and two League Cups.

3. Martin Keown became the first player to rejoin Arsenal post World War II following spells at Aston Villa and Everton either side of his lone season with the first team in the mid-1980s. His remarkably formidable center-back partnership with Tony Adams led the Gunners to league and FA Cup doubles in 1998 and 2002. He featured rather sporadically in his final season as Arsenal romped to the 2003/04 championship unbeaten.

4. Sol Campbell scored Arsenal's only goal in their only UEFA Champions League final appearance, a narrow 2-1 defeat at the hands of Spanish powerhouse FC Barcelona. He crossed the North London divide in 2001 to join Arsenal and won the League and FA Cup in his first season at Highbury. Partnered by a young Kolo Toure, he helped the club to another league title in 2003/04, remaining unbeaten for the entire league campaign.

5. Pat Rice appeared 528 times in Arsenal's red and scored 13 goals from 1967 to 1980. His debut season at right-back saw the North London club clinch an unprecedented League and FA Cup double. He became Arsenal skipper in 1977

following the departure of World Cup winner Alan Ball. He led the club to three successive FA Cup finals, winning it in 1979 and the UEFA Cup Winners Cup final in 1980, which the club lost to Valencia on penalties.

6. Ivorian defender Kolo Toure is one of a select few players to have won the Premier League with two different clubs. He is also among a much fewer group to have won league titles unbeaten with two different clubs, winning another title unbeaten with Celtic after his Arsenal days. His great partnership with Sol Campbell led Arsenal to that 'Invincible' season, a record 49 league games unbeaten, and a first UEFA Champions League final in 2006.

7. Nigel Winterburn was a member of the most famous backline in Arsenal history that comprised Tony Adams, Steve Bould, Lee Dixon, and David Seaman behind them in goal. The English left-back is considered by many as the greatest Arsenal player in his position due to his reliably consistent displays during a remarkably successful thirteen years at the club.

8. Lee Dixon made the fourth most appearances for Arsenal, turning out a remarkable 619 times. He is, without doubt, the greatest right back in Gunner's rich history. His astute positional awareness allowed him to bomb up and down the right flank without exposing himself defensively. He scored 28 times and won eight majors during his 15-year stay at Highbury.

9. Ashley Cole is still highly regarded among Arsenal faithful despite his acrimonious departure to join London rivals Chelsea in 2006. In a poll conducted by the Gunners' official website, Cole was placed 25th among the 50 greatest players in the club's history. Along with two league titles, Cole won three FA Cups with Arsenal and a further four at Chelsea to become the most decorated player in FA Cup history.

10. An injury crisis during the 1969/70 season prompted Arsenal coach Don Howe to move Frank McLintock into the heart of the defense. The Scotsman excelled and soon after was made captain. He helped Arsenal overturn a 3-1 first-leg deficit to clinch the Inter-Cities Fairs Cup against Anderlecht and a year later led Arsenal to a first League and FA Cup double.

MIDFIELDERS

"You can buy any strikers you want, but this position is important, and you need someone there who can do the job."

- Patrick Vieira

20 Trivia Questions

1. Where was Gilberto Silva signed from?

   A. Atletico Madrid

   B. Flamengo

   C. Atletico Miniero

   D. VfB Stuttgart

2. How many Premier League title(s) did Robert Pires win at Arsenal F.C.?

   A. 4

   B. 3

   C. 2

   D. 1

3. How many assists did Santi Cazorla record in his first season at Arsenal F.C.?

   A. 16 assists

   B. 14 assists

   C. 12 assists

   D. 10 assists

4. Which of these midfielders did not win the club's 2004/05 FA Cup?

    A. Cesc Fabregas

    B. Mathieu Flamini

    C. Gilberto Silva

    D. Abou Diaby

5. Which of these trophies did Liam Brady win with the club?

    A. First Division title

    B. FA Cup

    C. League Cup

    D. FA Charity Cup (Community Shield)

6. Which of these former Arsenal midfielders holds the record for "most red cards" among midfielders?

    A. Gilberto Silva

    B. Patrick Vieira

    C. Alex Song

    D. Francis Coquelin

7. How many goals did Robert Pires score in his first season at Arsenal?

    A. 10 goals

    B. 8 goals

    C. 6 goals

    D. 4 goals

8. Where was Patrick Vieira signed from?

   A. Monaco

   B. Fiorentina

   C. A.C Milan

   D. Sporting CP

9. How many assists did Mesut Ozil register in his maiden season at the club?

   A. 17 assists

   B. 15 assists

   C. 13 assists

   D. 11 assists

10. What is the nationality of Arsenal midfielder, Lucas Torreira?

    A. Paraguay

    B. Uruguay

    C. Argentina

    D. Bolivia

11. Which of these midfielders returned to the club as a head coach?

    A. Patrick Vieira

    B. Dennis Bergkamp

    C. Gilberto Silva

    D. Mikel Arteta

12. Which of these midfielders returned to the club as a technical director?

    A. Ian Wright

    B. Eduardo Gaspar

    C. Freddie Ljungberg

    D. Ray Parlour

13. How many FA Cups did Aaron Ramsey win with the club?

    A. 5

    B. 4

    C. 3

    D. 2

14. How long did Mesut Ozil take to register his first Premier League assist?

    A. 71 minutes

    B. 41 minutes

    C. 31 minutes

    D. 11 minutes

15. Which of these midfielders won the 1970 European Fairs' Cup with Arsenal?

    A. Peter Storey

    B. Michael Thomas

    C. David Jack

    D. Anders Limpar

16. Which of these midfielders did not feature in the 1990/91 league title-winning squad?

    A. Michael Thomas

    B. David Rocastle

    C. Paul Davis

    D. David Platt

17. Which of these Arsenal midfielders was nicknamed 'The Romford Pele'?

    A. David Rocastle

    B. Ray Parlour

    C. David Platt

    D. Gilberto Silva

18. Which of these midfielders did not win a trophy with the club?

    A. Denilson Neves

    B. Jermaine Pennant

    C. Eduardo Gasper

    D. Ray Parlour

19. Which club sold Granit Xhaka to Arsenal F.C.?

    A. Basel

    B. Benfica

    C. Borussia Monchengladbach

    D. Borussia Dortmund

20. Which Arsenal midfielder was nicknamed "The Little Mozart"?

    A. Mesut Ozil

    B. Santi Carzola

    C. Cesc Fabregas

    D. Tomas Rosicky

20 Trivia Answers

1. C – Atletico Mineiro

2. C – 2

3. B – 14 Assists

4. D – Abou Diaby

5. B – FA Cup

6. B – Patrick Vieira

7. A – 10 Goals

8. C – Milan

9. C – 13 Assists

10. B – Uruguay

11. D – Mikel Arteta

12. B – Eduardo Gasper

13. C – 3

14. D – 11 Minutes

15. A – Peter Storey

16. D – David Platt

17. B – Ray Parlour

18. A – Denilson Neves

19. C – Borussia Monchengladbach

20. D – Tomas Rosicky

10 Fun Facts

1. Patrick Vieira remains the last Arsenal captain to lead the club to championship glory, doing so undefeated in 2003/04. He is arguably the best midfielder in the club's history, having been at the centre of almost everything good the Gunners did between 1996 to 2005. His last ever kick for the club secured a 5-4 penalty shootout victory against Manchester United in the 2005 FA Cup final.

2. French World Cup and European Championship winner, Robert Pires, regularly reached double digits for goals and assist in each of his superbly impressive six seasons at Highbury. He helped Arsenal to two Premier League titles and three FA Cups, scoring the winner in a 1-0 FA Cup final win against Southampton in 2003.

3. Irish midfielder, Liam Brady, had almost everything needed in a midfielder; speed, agility, power, technique, vision, strength, and ability to get past the opposition easily. He made his Arsenal debut in 1973 and was part of the team that reached 3 successive FA Cup finals, winning it against Manchester United in 1979. He was voted PFA Player of the Year for 1979 and left for Juventus a year later.

4. Swedish midfielder, Fredrik 'Freddie' Ljungberg, capped a memorable Arsenal debut by grabbing a goal in a 3-0 rout of fierce title rivals Manchester United. He scored 17 goals as the Gunners completed a second League and FA Cup double in four years during the 2001/02 season. He was named player of the year and played a significant role in the Gunners' march to a third Premier League crown a couple of years later.

5. Ray Parlour made his first Gunners appearance in 1992 but did not feature very regularly until Arsene Wenger was handed the reins in 1996. He made over 400 appearances for the North London club and won three Premier League titles, four FA Cups, a League cup, and a Cup Winners Cup. Two of his most stellar performances for Arsenal came in the 1998 and 2002 FA Cup finals.

6. David "Rocky" Rocastle came through the youth ranks at Arsenal and went on to become one of the most influential midfielders in the club's history. Despite his injury worries, he made over 200 Gunners appearances and featured in every minute of the club's 1988/89 title-winning campaign. He helped the club to another title in 1991 before leaving for Leeds United a year later. He passed away at the young age of 33, having been diagnosed with non-Hodgkin's Lymphoma in 2000

7. Arsenal found a readymade replacement for departing club legend Patrick Vieira in Spanish wonderkid, Cesc Fabregas. Fabregas possessed excellent vision and was a product of FC Barcelona's talent-rich La Masia academy. He won the FA Cup with Arsenal in 2005 and played a sterling role in their run to the 2006 UEFA Champions League final. His tally of 111 Premier League assists is bettered only by the 162 of Ryan Giggs.

8. Pacey Dutch winger, Marc Overmars, became both the most expensive export by a British club and the most expensive import by a Spanish club when he completed a £25 million move from Arsenal to FC Barcelona in 2000. In the three years prior, he had helped Arsene Wenger's side to a Premier League and FA Cup double in the French manager's first full season. Overmars scored in the FA Cup final against Newcastle United.

9. A number of eye-catching performances at the 2002 Korea/Japan World Cup prompted Arsenal to acquire the services of Brazilian midfielder, Gilberto Silva, from Atletico Miniero. The World Cup winner immediately kickstarted his Gunners career with the winning goal against Liverpool in the 2002 Community Shield. His virtuoso performances in front of a solid back four helped Arsenal two FA Cups and a Premier League title in his first three seasons at the club.

10. Santi Cazorla had already dazzled with Villareal and Malaga before moving to the Emirates in 2012. Goals against Liverpool and Tottenham early in his Arsenal career helped endear him to the Gunners fans. His incredible technique and splendid vision helped the club end a nine-year trophy drought with a FA cup triumph in 2014. Two more FA cups followed in 2015 and 2017 before he left in 2018 at the end of his contract.

FORWARDS

"What makes the difference between a great player and just a normal player is dedication, work, and commitment."

- Thierry Henry

20 Trivia Questions

1. Who is the highest-ever goal scorer for Arsenal?

    A. Theirry Henry

    B. Ian Wright

    C. Robin Van Persie

    D. Dennis Bergkamp

2. How many matches did it take Thierry Henry to score his first goal for Arsenal?

    A. 2

    B. 4

    C. 5

    D. 7

3. From which club was Ian Wright signed?

    A. Greenwich

    B. Celtic

    C. Crystal Palace

    D. Westham

4. How many goals did Nwankwo Kanu score for Arsenal?

    A. 86

    B. 56

    C. 98

    D. 44

5. Which team did Arsenal record their first Champions League hat-trick against?

    A. Inter Milan

    B. FC Basel

    C. Galatasaray

    D. AS Roma

6. Who was the first Arsenal striker to score a Champions League Hattrick?

    A. Nikolas Bendtner

    B. Thierry Henry

    C. Danny Welbeck

    D. Oliver Giroud

7. Against which club did Emmanuel Adebayo score his first goal for Arsenal?

    A. Manchester United

    B. Sheffield United

    C. Birmingham City

    D. Sunderland

8. In his last season at Arsenal, how many goals did Robin Van Persie score?

    A. 30

    B. 35

    C. 33

    D. 32

9. How many goals did Oliver Giroud score for Arsenal?

    A. 98

    B. 105

    C. 109

    D. 110

10. Who were the opponents when Julio Baptista scored his first hat trick for Arsenal?

    A. Bolton Wanderers

    B. Norwich City

    C. Aston Villa

    D. Liverpool

11. In his debut season for Arsenal, how many goals did Ian Wright score?

    A. 14

    B. 19

    C. 28

    D. 24

12. Who scored the winning goal against Manchester united in the 2015 FA Cup Round 6?

 A. Danny Welbeck

 B. Aaron Ramsey

 C. Oliver Giroud

 D. Mesut Ozil

13. Which club did Kanu leave Arsenal for?

 A. Portsmouth

 B. Ajax

 C. West Brom

 D. Inter Milan

14. How many goals did Alexis Sanchez score in the 2016/17 season?

 A. 42

 B. 30

 C. 36

 D. 29

15. Who was the highest goal scorer in the Invincibles season?

 A. Theirry Henry

 B. Dennis Bergkamp

 C. Robert Pires

 D. Nwankwo Kanu

16. Which of these French clubs sold Emmanual Adebayor to Arsenal?

    A. Lille

    B. Rennes

    C. Marseille

    D. Monaco

17. How many goals did Eduardo score for Arsenal?

    A. 21

    B. 34

    C. 50

    D. 32

18. From which club was Eduardo signed?

    A. Dynamo Zagreb

    B. Shakhtar Donetsk

    C. Flamengo

    D. Santos

19. Before he joined Arsenal, where was Nicolas Anelka starring?

    A. Paris Saint Germaine

    B. Lille

    C. Rennes

    D. Lorient

20. How many goals did Nikolas Bendtner score in total for Arsenal?

    A. 50

    B. 65

    C. 47

    D. 62

20 Trivia Answers

1. A – Theirry Henry

2. D – 7

3. C – Crystal Palace

4. D – 44

5. DAS Roma

6. B – Thierry Henry

7. C – Birmingham City

8. A – 30

9. B – 105

10. D – Liverpool

11. D – 24

12. D – Danny Welbeck

13. C – West Brom

14. B – 30

15. A – Theirry Henry

16. D – Monaco

17. A – 21

18. A – Dynamo Zagreb

19. A – Paris Saint Germaine

20. C – 47

10 Fun Facts

1. In the 2011/2012 campaign, Robin Van Persie became the second Arsenal player to score 30 league goals in one season. The only other Gunner to accomplish this feat is Thierry Henry, who did so in the Invincible campaign of 2003/04.

2. The legendary Henry was not just a goal scorer. He was fast, technical, and swift-footed. He had an unequaled knack for both creating and finishing them. His record of 24 goals and 20 assists from 37 league appearances in 2002/03 remains unbroken.

3. Other accomplishments by Thierry Henry (at Arsenal) include most goals in one stadium (114 in 175 league games at the Highbury stadium), the only player (with Sergio Kun Aguero) to score more than 20 goals in 5 consecutive EPL seasons, the runner up for the Ballon d'Or (2003 and 2004) and arguably the best striker the EPL has ever seen.

4. Pierre-Emerick Aubameyang reached 22 league goals in the 2018/19 season. He repeated that feat in the next season. In total, Gabonese international scored 68 goals in 128 for the Gunners, with a relatively high goals-to-match ratio of 0.53.

5. Despite his injury struggles and infamous departure, Arsenal fans will remember Robin Van Persie as the 8th highest goal scorer in the club's history and one of the best "number 9s" in the history of the game. He scored 132 goals in 278 matches (96 in 194 league games), many of which were memorable.

6. Dennis Bergkamp's nickname, "The non-flying Dutchman," comes from his fear of flying. However, defenders could barely cope with his skill, vision, and creativity on the pitch. After 11 years of service, Bergkamp left Arsenal as a legend with 120 goals in 432 games, and 11 trophies.

7. Before Thierry Henry, Arsenal had Ian Wright to put the ball into the back of the net. And boy, did he know how? He hit 185 goals in 288 games. He may not have been as skillful as Henry, but by the time he left the Highbury, Wright had 2 FA cups, 1 EPL title, and a League Cup to his name.

8. Oliver Giroud may be known more for his link-up play and strength in the air than for beautiful goals. However, in 2017, he won the FIFA Puskas Award for an outrageous overhead scorpion kick that completed a flowing team-centric counter-attacking move while playing for Arsenal.

9. Many young Gunners may not know the tall and skillful Nigerian Kanu Nwankwo, even though he won 2 FA cup and 2 EPL titles at the club. But his goal to complete a hat trick against Chelsea at Stamford Bridge remains one of the best in the history of the Premier League. After getting past his marker, he curled a finish in from a frankly impossible angle.

10. Nicknamed "Baby Kanu", Emmanuel Adebayor was signed in January 2006 from Monaco. In the 2006/07 season, he scored his first hattrick against Derby County in a 5-0 romp at the Emirates. On 28th April, 2008, he scored another hattrick against the same opponents in a 6-2 win. He is the only EPL player to score a hattrick against the same opponent home and away in the same season.

CAPTAINS

"Play for the name on the front of the shirt, and they will remember the name on the back."

- Tony Adams

20 Trivia Questions

1. Who is the longest-serving captain of Arsenal?

    A. Pat Rice

    B. Bill Julain

    C. Laurent Koscielny

    D. Tony Adams

2. Who was the captain during the Invincibles season?

    A. Tony Adams

    B. Patrick Viera

    C. Thierry Henry

    D. Dennis Bergkamp

3. Who captained Arsenal in the 2006 Champions League final?

    A. Robin Van Persie

    B. Thierry Henry

    C. Cesc Fabregas

    D. Kolo Toure

4. Who was the first captain to win the League Cup for the club?

   A. Kenny Samson

   B. Pat Rice

   C. Adam Bill

   D. Tony Adams

5. Who was the captain for the 2001/2002 Premier League season?

   A. Patrick Viera

   B. Tony Adams

   C. Billy Bates

   D. Alf Baker

6. Who is the third youngest-ever player to serve as permanent captain at Arsenal?

   A. Tony Adams

   B. Cesc Fabregas

   C. Robin Van Persie

   D. Jack Wilshere

7. Who was the Captain for Arsene Wenger's final home game?

   A. Per Mertesacker

   B. Granit Xhaka

   C. Petr Cech

   D. Laurent Koscielny

8. Who captained Arsenal in the 2016/17 FA Cup final?

    A. Per Mertesacker

    B. Laurent Koscielny

    C. Mikel Arteta

    D. Granit Xhaka

9. Who is the current captain of Arsenal?

    A. Pierre-Emeric Aubameyang

    B. Alexandre Lacazette

    C. Granit Xhaka

    D. Rob Holding

10. Who was the last player to captain Arsenal in the Champions League?

    A. Per Mertesacker

    B. Laurent Koscielny

    C. Mikel Arteta

    D. Granit Xhaka

11. Who was the captain of Arsenal at the Baku Europa League final?

    A. Mikel Arteta

    B. Granit Xhaka

    C. Laurent Koscielny

    D. Per Mertesacker

12. Who was the captain of the Arsenal side to win their first English Premier League?

    A. Tony Adams

    B. Steve Bould

    C. Lee Dixon

    D. Nigel Winterburn

13. Who was the captain of Arsenal when they won their first FA Cup?

    A. Billy Blyth

    B. Charlie Jones

    C. Tom Parker

    D. Charlie Buchan

14. Who was the captain of the Arsenal team that won the first FA Cup under Wenger?

    A. Lee Dixon

    B. Tony Adams

    C. Steve Bould

    D. Charlie Buchan

15. Which of these captains won the Premier League and FA Cup double at Arsenal?

    A. Patrick Viera

    B. Tony Adams

    C. Steve Bould

    D. Frank McLintock

16. Who was the first Arsenal captain?

    A. Arthur Brown

    B. Bill Julian

    C. David Danskin

    D. Moris Bates

17. Which of these Arsenal captains left for Juventus?

    A. Patrick Viera

    B. Thierry Henry

    C. Moris Bates

    D. Charlie Buchan

18. What was the span of Tony Adams' captaincy?

    A. 1985-2002

    B. 1989-2002

    C. 1988-2002

    D. 1990-2002

19. Who captained the FA Cup-winning team of 1998?

    A. Patrick Viera

    B. Tony Adams

    C. Steve Bould

    D. Charlie Buchan

20. Who was the captain of the team that won the first Community Shield?

   A. Billy Blyth

   B. Tom Parker

   C. Alex Barker

   D. Alf Baker

20 Trivia Answers

1. D – Tony Adams

2. B – Patrick Viera

3. B - Thierry Henry

4. A – Kenny Samson

5. B – Tony Adams

6. A – Tony Adams

7. C – Petr Cech

8. A – Per Mertesacker

9. B – Alexandre Lacazette

10. B – Laurent Koscielny

11. C – Laurent Koscielny

12. A – Tony Adams

13. C – Tom Parker

14. B – Tony Adams

15. B – Tony Adams

16. C – David Danskin

17. A – Patrick Viera

18. C – 1988-2002

19. B – Tony Adams

20. B – Tom Parker

10 Fun Facts

1. The first player to captain Arsenal Football Club was a goalkeeper called David Danskin. He was a founding member of the club and a part-time mechanical engineer.

2. Tony Adams is the club's longest-serving skipper (14 years, from 1988 to 2002). Adams is a one-club player, which earned him the name "MR Arsenal." He played 669 competitive matches and won 10 trophies.

3. Patrick Vieira succeeded Tony Adams and captained the club during its most successful spell (2002 to 2005) of the Premier League era. He also ended his Arsenal on a high note, scoring the winning penalty to win the 2004/2005 FA cup title against rivals, Manchester United. He left, having won 3 EPL, 5 FA Cups, and 3 English super cup titles.

4. After Vieira, Thierry Henry took up the captain's armband. The team reached the UEFA Champions League final for the first time with him. However, on an emotionally-charged night that saw goalkeeper, Jens Lehmann sent off, Arsenal lost 2-1 to Barcelona

5. The youngest player to captain the gunners is Terry Neill, who was 20 years and 102 days at the time. He made his debut against Sheffield Wednesday at eighteen years old in December 1960 and was made captain two years later in 1962.

6. The second-youngest player to captain Arsenal is Cesc Fabregas, who took on the role at 21 years and 204 days. He led Arsenal back into Champions League football, including a semi-final berth in 2008/09.

7. William Gallas was made captain After Patrick Vieira. However, he became known for letting his emotions get the best of him and criticizing his young teammates instead of setting up a good example for them. As captain, his most scandalous actions include sitting on the pitch to cry after a draw at Birmingham City in 2008 and saying his young teammates were "not brave enough" in an interview.

8. Mikel Arteta's two seasons as captain were the worst years he had in the Arsenal jersey. He missed many games due to injury and inconsistent form before retiring in 2016. He has since returned to Arsenal as the current coach of the side.

9. The undesired award of the shortest captaincy spell in the history of Arsenal FC goes to Granit Xhaka. He lasted for barely three months before being stripped of the armband after he reacted poorly when booed by fans during a draw at home against Crystal Palace.

10. Robin Van Persie was only club captain for one season before leaving for Manchester United. During that one season, he scored 37 goals, led his team to a third-place league position, and won the trio of the most important individual awards in English football – the Golden Boot, Football Writers Player of the Year, and PFA Player's Player of the year.

TITLES

"At some clubs success is accidental. At Arsenal it is compulsory."

- Arsene Wenger

20 Trivia Questions

1. How many European honours does Arsenal have?

    A. 0

    B. 1

    C. 2

    D. 3

2. How many years have Arsenal gone without winning the Premier League?

    A. 19

    B. 20

    C. 18

    D. 17

3. How many Premier League titles have Arsenal won?

    A. 3

    B. 4

    C. 5

    D. 10

4. How many League titles (in total) does Arsenal have?

    A. 16

    B. 15

    C. 13

    D. 12

5. How many times have Arsenal won the FA Cup?

    A. 12

    B. 14

    C. 15

    D. 11

6. How many Community Shields have Arsenal won?

    A. 12

    B. 5

    C. 19

    D. 16

7. Against which team did Arsenal win her 10th FA Cup final?

    A. Chelsea

    B. Westham United

    C. Manchester United

    D. Liverpool

8. What was the scoreline in the club's 13th FA cup final win?

   A. 2-1

   B. 3-0

   C. 1-1

   D. 4-2

9. What is Arsenal's biggest win in an FA Cup final?

   A. 3-2

   B. 4-1

   C. 5-2

   D. 4-0

10. How many FA Cup and League double has Arsenal won?

   A. 1

   B. 2

   C. 4

   D. 3

11. How many trophies have Arsenal won in the Emirate Stadium era?

   A. 2

   B. 4

   C. 6

   D. 8

12. What was the last trophy won at the Highbury Stadium?

    A. The FA Cup

    B. The Premier League

    C. The Carling Cup

    D. The Champions League

13. What was the first major trophy won at the Emirates?

    A. The Carling Cup

    B. The FA Cup

    C. The Community Shield

    D. The Premier League

14. Against what team did Arsenal enjoy their biggest FA Cup final win?

    A. Hull City

    B. Manchester United

    C. Aston Villa

    D. Chelsea

15. How many times have Arsenal been an FA Cup final runner-up?

    A. 10

    B. 7

    C. 8

    D. 9

16. What was the scoreline of the club's 11th FA Cup final win?

    A. 3:2

    B. 2:1

    C. 3:0

    D. 1:0

17. How many times have Arsenal won back-to-back FA Cups?

    A. 4

    B. 3

    C. 2

    D. 1

18. How many times have Arsenal won back-to-back League titles?

    A. 2

    B. 3

    C. 1

    D. 4

19. How many consecutive league titles have Arsenal won?

    A. 4

    B. 3

    C. 2

    D. 1

20. How many back-to-back Community Shield titles has Arsenal won?

    A. 1

    B. 2

    C. 3

    D. 4

20 Trivia Answers

1. C – 2

2. D – 17

3. A – 3

4. C – 13

5. B – 14

6. D – 16

7. C – Manchester United

8. A – 2:1

9. D – 4:0

10. D – 3

11. D – 8

12. A – The FA Cup

13. B – FA Cup

14. C – Aston Villa

15. B – 7

16. A – 3:2

17. C – 2

18. A – 2

19. B – 3

20. C – 3

10 Fun Facts

1. With 14 wins, Arsenal FC are the kings of the FA cup. They won it for the first time in 1930 and their most recent win was in 2020.

2. The first title the club ever won was the Kent Junior Cup, won by the reserve team. However, the first team was not to be outdone. Just three weeks later, they also won the Kent seniors cup.

3. Arsenal FC has accomplished the league and cup double three times. It did this in the 1970/71, 1997/98, and 2001/02 seasons. Arsenal is yet the accomplish the bigger feat of a domestic treble. However, they also won the FA and League Cup double in 1992/93.

4. Arsenal has played in the final for the League Cup 8 times, winning twice (1986/87 and 1992/93). They have also competed in the FA community shield 23 times, winning on 16 occasions. The first win was in 1930, while the latest was a penalty shootout against Liverpool in 2020.

5. Although Arsenal is yet to win the UEFA champions league and Europa Cup, they have reached the final once (2005/06) and twice (1999/00 and 2018/19) respectively.

6. However, this doesn't mean that Arsenal doesn't have European titles. They have two – the Inter-Cities Fairs Cup (1970) and the European Cup Winners' Cup (1994). However, rival fans like to neglect these trophies because they are not UEFA's.

7. In total, the trophy cabinet at Arsenal holds 30 major trophies. This includes English first division titles, FA Cups, and league cups among others.

8. Since the departure of the legendary Arsene Wenger, the club has only added two major trophies to its collection. This includes the FA cup (2019/20) and the Community shield (2020). Both were won by former club captain and current manager, Mikel Arteta.

9. Arsenal has won 13 English league titles, including 3 Premier League titles. Arsenal ended the 20th century with the highest average league position among all English top flight clubs.

10. The 2003/04 league title win is the greatest in the history of Arsenal F.C. Arsenal went an entire 38 matches season undefeated on their way to the title, the only English club to achieve the feat. The unbeaten run formed a part of a larger 49 matches unbeaten run which ended the next season against Manchester United. Arsenal F.C received a golden trophy for this great feat and the team was fondly referred to as "the Invincibles."

MEMORABLE GAMES

"I tried to watch the Tottenham match on television in my hotel yesterday, but I fell asleep."

- Arsene Wenger

20 Trivia Questions

1. Who were the first opponents at the new Emirates stadium?

   A. Ajax

   B. Aston Villa

   C. Westham

   D. Stoke City

2. What is the highest attendance figure at the Emirate stadium?

   A. 59,232

   B. 60,161

   C. 61,543

   D. 58,765

3. What was the scoreline for the biggest defeat suffered by Arsenal in the Premier League?

   A. 8:2

   B. 6:0

   C. 7:1

   D. 8:0

4. What was the scoreline for Arsenal's biggest win in the Champions League?

    A. 6:0

    B. 8:0

    C. 7:0

    D. 11:2

5. Which of these players famously confessed to throwing a pizza at Sir Alex Ferguson of Manchester United during the infamous Pizzagate scandal?

    A. Patrick Vieira

    B. Kolo Toure

    C. Cesc Fabregas

    D. Robert Pires

6. What was the scoreline for Arsenal's biggest win in the FA Cup?

    A. 12:0

    B. 11:1

    C. 10:2

    D. 13:0

7. Who were the last opponents at the Highbury stadium?

    A. Derby County

    B. Wigan Athletic

    C. Bolton Wanderers

    D. Stoke City

8. Which team handed Arsenal the club's biggest defeat in the FA Cup?

    A.   Bolton Athletic

    B.   Sunderland

    C.   Liverpool

    D.   Derby County

9. What was the scoreline of the highest-scoring North London derby between Arsenal and Tottenham Hotspurs?

    A.   4:3

    B.   6:0

    C.   5:4

    D.   4:4

10. Arsenal defeated Spurs in the September 2021 derby at the Emirates. What was the scoreline?

    A.   3:1

    B.   3:0

    C.   1:0

    D.   4:0

11. Which team ended Arsenal's record 49 matches unbeaten run?

    A.   Chelsea

    B.   Manchester United

    C.   Sunderland

    D.   Manchester City

12. Which team did Arsenal start their 49 matches unbeaten Premier League run against?

    A. Wigan Athletic

    B. Southampton

    C. Sunderland

    D. Middlesbrough

13. Who were the UCL opponents when Arsenal fielded 11 players of different nationalities in 2006?

    A. Hamburg S.V

    B. Borussia Dortmund

    C. Valencia C.F

    D. Liverpool F.C

14. On February 14, 2005, Arsenal fielded an all-foreign squad of players. Who were the opponents?

    A. Leeds United

    B. Southampton F.C

    C. Crystal Palace

    D. West Bromwich Albion

15. Which team did Arsenal play their first Champions League match against?

    A. RC Lens

    B. Inter Milan

    C. Standard Liege

    D. Lyon

16. Arsenal required a comeback to win the 2013/14 FA Cup final. What was the initial scoreline?

    A. 2:0

    B. 3:0

    C. 1:0

    D. 4:0

17. Who scored Arsenal's first goal in their comeback in the 2013/14 FA Cup Final?

    A. Alex Iwobi

    B. Aaron Ramsey

    C. Santi Cazorla

    D. Laurent Koscielny

18. What was the scoreline for Arsenal's biggest home win against Tottenham Hotspurs in the PL era?

    A. 5:1

    B. 4:2

    C. 5:2

    D. 6:2

19. What was the scoreline for Arsenal's biggest away win against Chelsea?

    A. 6:0

    B. 5:1

    C. 7:2

    D. 5:0

20. What was the scoreline for Arsenal's biggest away win against Tottenham Hotspurs?

    A. 5:2

    B. 6:0

    C. 4:3

    D. 7:1

20 Trivia Answers

1. A – Ajax

2. B – 60,161

3. A – 8:2

4. C – 7:0

5. C – Cesc Fabregas

6. B – 11:1

7. B – Wigan Athletic

8. B – Sunderland

9. C – 5:4

10. A – 3:1

11. B – Manchester United

12. B – Southampton

13. A – Hamburg SV

14. C – Crystal Palace

15. A – RC Lens

16. A – 2:0

17. C – Santi Cazorla

18. C – 5:2

19. B – 5:1

20. B – 6:0

10 Fun Facts

1. Today, Arsenal is the king of the English FA Cup, but they had to start somewhere. That was in the 1929/30 season with a 2-0 win over Huddersfield Town. However, that first major trophy is not the only thing that makes this match important to Arsenal fans and all lovers of football alike. This was the first match that the BBC ever paid for the broadcasting rights. So, it is technically the beginning of the league's lucrative television rights.

2. Football has more than enough thrilling competition finals, but very few are so incredible that even fans of the losing team applaud and celebrate the winners. In the 1970/71 season, Arsenal beat Liverpool 2-1 in the final of the FA Cup to cement their first domestic (league/cup) double. They came from behind, scoring both goals late on and match-winner, Charlie George, gave us the iconic "lying down on my back" jubilation.

3. In 2013/14, after nine years without a trophy, Arsenal regained the FA cup crown by condemning Hull City to a 3-2 defeat. Hull City were the underdogs but the final was no walkover. Ten minutes after the kickoff, the Gunners were down by two goals. They fought back through Santi Cazorla, equalized through Laurent Koscielny and sent the game into extra time where Aaron Ramsey popped up 11 minutes to the end to win the game.

4. Memorable footballing moments are not just about glee. Pain is also part of the beautiful game. The Gunners will always remember their 2005/06 loss to FC Barcelona in the UEFA Champions League final. Arsenal scored first, despite being down to 10 men after Jens Lehman was sent off. However, goals from Samuel Eto and Belletti gave Barcelona the win.

5. On May 7, 2006, Arsenal played their last match at Highbury, and it was a worthy send-off. Ninety-three years of passion and history were bookended with a thrilling 4-2 win against Wigan Athletic. The match also had high stakes because Arsenal needed a positive result to pip crosstown rival, Tottenham

Hotspur to the final UEFA champions league qualifying position. From 2 goals down, Arsenal turned the game around courtesy of a Thierry Henry hat trick.

6. The 1988/89 league season was decided almost like a cup final. Title rivals Liverpool and Arsenal were playing each other at Anfield in the last match of the season with the latter requiring a win by at least two goals to win the title. Liverpool had not lost by two goals in close to three years and they were clear favorites. Arsenal brought in David O'Leary to act as a sweeper and stem the potent Liverpool attack. Star striker, Alan Smith, gave Arsenal the lead but it was not until Michael Thomas's stoppage time goal that the title finally swung decisively in favor of the North London side.

7. The last time Arsenal won a league/cup double was in 2002, and it came via a 1-0 win against Manchester United at Old Trafford. Arsenal went into the game with an unbeaten away record and having already wrapped up the league. However, they were missing key players like Thierry Henry, Denis Bergkamp, Robert Pires, and Mr. Arsenal himself, Tony Adams. Yet, they managed to secure the trophy after a goal by Freddie Ljungberg.

8. Thierry Henry is one of the best attackers ever to play the beautiful game, but some people had initial doubts about his prowess against elite European oppositions. Every doubt died on November 25, 2003, a day that Henry destroyed a strong Inter Milan defense, scoring two and creating two more. Arsenal came into the game on the back of zero wins in their first 3 group games. They left the San Siro with a 5-1 victory.

9. In 2020, behind Wembley Stadium closed doors (due to the Covid-19 pandemic), Arsenal won 2-1 against Liverpool to lift the FA cup once again. This game is important for several reasons. It was the first major trophy since the glory days of the Arsene Wenger era, and it brought hope of a new beginning. It was also a match of legacies with both teams being managed by club legends who had both won the FA Cup at the clubs, Frank Lampard (Chelsea, 4) and Mikel Arteta (Arsenal, 2). Arsenal also needed the win to qualify for European football. Chelsea took the initial lead, but a double by Aubameyang gave the Gunners the last laugh.

10. On May 21, 2005, Arsenal and Manchester United squared up in the FA cup final. Manchester United showed an extra edge in the match held in Cardiff but

Arsenal held on for a penalty shootout with a gusty performance. Paul Scholes missed the decisive kick and Arsenal added yet another FA cup title to their trophy cabinet.

BIGGEST TRANSFERS
(HIDDEN GEMS AND MASSIVE DEALS)

*"When Patrick Vieira came over from AC Milan, he didn't
know a word of English. We gave him accommodation,
phone, car & an English teacher. I talked to Patrick in
fluent French and before a game I asked in French, can you
speak a bit of English to me? Patrick nodded and replied,
'Tottenham are shit'."*

- David Dein

20 Trivia Questions

1. Who is the most expensive January Signing Arsenal has ever made?

    A. Nicolas Pepe

    B. Alexandre Lacazette

    C. Pierre Emerick Aubameyang

    D. Ben White

2. Arsene Wenger once said, "I'm sorry he didn't cost 50M pounds". Which player was he referring to?

    A. Rob Holding

    B. Mikel Arteta

    C. Per Mertesacker

    D. Hector Bellerin

3. Who is the most expensive signing in Arsenal history?

    A. Nicolas Pepe

    B. Ben White

    C. Aaron Ramsdale

    D. Alexandre Lacazette

4. Who holds the record for the most expensive Arsenal defender?

    A. Gabriel Magalhaes

    B. Ben White

    C. Shkodran Mustafi

    D. Kierien Tierney

5. Who was the most expensive defender signed under Arsene Wenger?

    A. Laurent Koscielny

    B. Per Mertesacker

    C. Sol Campbel

    D. Shkodran Mustafi

6. Which of these players left Arsenal for Chelsea in an acrimonious deal?

    A. Willian Gallas

    B. Ashley Cole

    C. Oliver Giroud

    D. Petr Cech

7. Who is the most expensive goalkeeper in Arsenal's history?

    A. Bernd Leno

    B. Jens Lehman

    C. Aaron Ramsdale

    D. David Ospina

8. Which player was involved in Arsenal's biggest transfer to Real Madrid?

    A. Nicolas Anelka

    B. Marc Overmas

    C. Lasana Diara

    D. Emmanuel Petit

9. Who is the most expensive sale in Arsenal's history?

    A. Alex Iwobi

    B. Thierry Henry

    C. Alex Oxlade Chamberlain

    D. Cesc Fabregas

10. From what club did Arsenal sign Cesc Fabregas?

    A. Mallorca

    B. Barcelona

    C. Sevilla

    D. Bilboa

11. Where did Arsenal sign Sol Campbell from?

    A. Blackburn Rovers

    B. Newcastle United

    C. Tottenham Hotspurs

    D. Stoke City

12. Where was Shkodran Mustafi signed from?

    A. Valencia C.F

    B. Schalke F.C

    C. Borussia Dortmund

    D. Mainz

13. Who was the first Asian player signed by Arsenal?

    A. Tokumo Asano

    B. Junichi Inamoto

    C. Takehiro Tomiyasu

    D. Riyo Miyachi

14. Who is the second most expensive Arsenal signing of all time?

    A. Ben White

    B. Alexander Lacazette

    C. Pierre Emerick Aubameyang

    D. Nicolas Pepe

15. From which French club did Arsenal sign Nicolas Pepe?

    A. Lille

    B. Monaco

    C. Auxerre

    D. Toulouse

16. Which of these players is considered the biggest player from the Hale End Academy?

    A.   Jack Wilshere

    B.   Bukayo Saka

    C.   Cesc Fabregas

    D.   Emile Smith Rowe

17. What is Arsenal's record for the highest number of signings in a single transfer window?

    A.   6

    B.   5

    C.   7

    D.   8

18. Who was Arsene Wenger's first signing as Arsenal manager?

    A.   Nicolas Anelka

    B.   Theirry Henry

    C.   Marc Overmars

    D.   Patrick Viera

19. Who was Mikel Arteta's first signing as Arsenal manager?

    A.   Omar Rekik

    B.   Gabriel Magalhaes

    C.   Gabriel Martinelli

    D.   Nuno Taveras

20. Who was Unai Emery's first signing at Arsenal?

   A.   Stephan Lichtsteiner

   B.   Nicolas Pepe

   C.   Kierian Tierney

   D.   Dani Ceballos

20 Trivia Answers

1. C – Pierre Emerick Aubameyang

2. A – Rob Holding

3. A – Nicolas Pepe

4. B – Ben White

5. D – Shkodran Mustafi

6. B – Ashley Cole

7. C – Aaron Ramsdale

8. A – Nicolas Anelka

9. C – Alex Oxlade Chamberlain

10. B – Barcelona

11. C – Tottenham Hotspurs

12. A – Valencia

13. B – Junichi Inamoto

14. C – Pierre Emerick Aubameyang

15. A – Lille

16. A – Jack Wilshere

17. D – 8

18. A – Nicolas Anelka

19. A – Omar Rekik

20. A – Stephan Lichtsteiner

10 Fun Facts

1. The club's transfer record belongs to Nicolas Pepe (from Lille), who cost Arsenal £72 million in the summer of 2019. The next biggest transfer was when Aubameyang was signed for £56m from Borussia Dortmund.

2. The highest fee that Arsenal has ever gotten for a player is the £40m that Liverpool paid in 2017 to sign attacking midfielder Alex Oxlade-Chamberlain. The main thrust for the transfer was as a result of Chamberlain's desire to play a central midfield position rather than in the wings where he had made a name for himself.

3. Frenchman, Robert Pires, will forever have a prominent position in the history of Arsenal. Signing him from Olympic Marseille in 2000 cost only £6 million, but he went on to net 62 goals in 189 appearances and was a pivotal member of the most successful Premier League era for Arsenal FC. To put things in perspective, the record for that year was the £37 million that Real Madrid paid Barcelona to sign Luis Figo.

4. Arsene Wenger was not known for spending a lot of money in the transfer market. He only broke the bank on a few occasions on special talents like Alexandre Lacazette, Aubameyang, and Mesut Ozil. Ozil suited Wenger's team spectacularly with his best return of 6 goals and 18 assists in 35 games during the 2015/2016 season. He scored 33 goals and created 54 assists in 189 games in an Arsenal jersey.

5. It took only £150,000 to bring Kolo Toure to the Highbury, He may not be as renowned as his brother, Yaya, but Kolo was a big part of the Gunner's defense for many years. He formed solid parings with fellow impressive defenders like Sol Campbell and William Gallas. He was a mainstay in the Invincibles team that conquered all before them. Toure left for Manchester City on bad terms, but Arsenal still turned a profit by selling him for £14 million.

6. On July 24th, 2013, Arsenal made one of the most infamous bids in the history of the sport when they offered Liverpool £40,000,001 for striker, Luiz Suarez. Arsene Wenger believed he had an agreement with the player and his agent, who had told him that his client's Liverpool contract contained a £40m release clause. The bid made Liverpool's owner, John W. Henry to tweet *"What do you think they're smoking over there at Emirates?"* Suarez eventually left for Barcelona in a £73.5m pounds deal.

7. Arsenal has a Zlatan story – it seems every top club has at least one. In 2000, at the age of 16, Zlatan Ibrahimovic almost signed for the Gunners. Wenger wanted to see his performance in a trial but Zlatan refused. According to the big Swede himself, he rebuffed the idea. *"I went to London for an appointment with Wenger, who asked me to audition for the Gunners. I told him 'I will not do a trial: either you take me or not, I'm not here to waste time."*

8. Thierry Henry will go down as arguably the best transfer decision in the club's history. Arsenal paid £11 million for the forward while he was struggling at Juventus. Even then, his introduction to life at Highbury was underwhelming as he went eight games without netting. However, the first goal opened the flood gates and he netted 26 goals in his debut season. The next season, he recorded 42 goals on Arsenal's way to the Double. Multiple FWA and PFA Player of the Year awards do not even paint an accurate picture of this lethal finisher who was just as adept at creating chances as scoring them. 228 goals later and that £11 million looked like a bargain.

9. Not every player breaks the Real Madrid transfer record but Nicolas Anelka is one of them. When you consider the fact that Nicolas Anelka was signed for only half-a-million pounds, that becomes even more impressive. In his time at Arsenal, Nicolas matured into a coldblooded finisher and within a few seasons, his transfer value had soared high. He went on to play for many top clubs including Manchester City, Chelsea, PSG and Liverpool.

10. In 1990, George Graham brought the greatest goalkeeper in Arsenal's history to the club. In his first season, David Seaman conceded only 18 goals and set the standards for other goalkeepers for the next decade-and-a-half. In fact, in the 1998/99 season, he only conceded 17 goals. You know your goalkeeper is good when Peter Schmeichel, an arch rival calls one of his saves "the best I've ever seen."

RECORD BREAKERS

"I am obsessed by the idea of making my mark on history and Arsenal is my paradise"

- Thierry Henry

20 Trivia Questions

1. Which of these Arsenal players has been voted into the top three positions for the Balon D'Or?

   A. Thierry Henry

   B. Robert Pires

   C. Tony Adams

   D. Robin Van Persie

2. Who holds the record for most goals for Arsenal?

   A. Ian Wright

   B. Thierry Henry

   C. Dennis Bergkamp

   D. Robert Pires

3. Who holds the record for most wins in the Premier League for Arsenal?

   A. Thierry Henry

   B. Tony Adams

   C. Dennis Bergkamp

   D. Ray Palour

4. What is Arsenal's longest run of matches without a win?

   A. 10

   B. 8

   C. 6

   D. 4

5. What is the longest unbeaten run by Arsenal in the Premier League in a season?

   A. 38

   B. 49

   C. 34

   D. 27

6. How long was Arsenal's longest unbeaten away run in the Premier League?

   A. 35

   B. 40

   C. 27

   D. 15

7. As at the end of the 2020/21 season, how many Premier League penalties had been scored by Arsenal?

   A. 90

   B. 80

   C. 76

   D. 60

8. Which of these players holds the record for most FA Cup appearances for Arsenal?

    A. Tony Adams

    B. David O'Leary

    C. David Seaman

    D. Thierry Henry

9. Who is the player who holds the record for most appearances for Arsenal?

    A. Tony Adams

    B. Lee Dixon

    C. David O'Leary

    D. David Seaman

10. Who holds the record for most goals in a single season for Arsenal?

    A. Thierry Henry

    B. Ian Wright

    C. Ted Drake

    D. Cliff Bastin

11. Patrick Viera holds the record for most Red Cards received by an Arsenal player in the Premier League. How many red cards did he receive?

    A. 2

    B. 3

    C. 8

    D. 5

12. Who was the first player to be sent off at the Emirates Stadium?

    A.   Ivan Campo

    B.   Phillipe Senderos

    C.   Pascal Cygan

    D.   Sol Campbell

13. Who is the youngest-ever player to score for Arsenal?

    A.   Jack Wilshere

    B.   Arturo Lupoli

    C.   Aaron Ramsey

    D.   Cesc Fabregas

14. Who is the oldest player to score for Arsenal?

    A.   Lee Dixon

    B.   Nigel Winterburn

    C.   Dennis Bergkamp

    D.   Jock Rutherford

15. Who is the youngest player to play for Arsenal?

    A.   Serge Gnabry

    B.   Cesc Fabregas

    C.   Smith Rowe

    D.   Jack Wilshere

16. Who holds the record for most Yellow Cards for Arsenal in the Premier League?

    A. Granit Xhaka

    B. Tony Adams

    C. Patrick Viera

    D. Sol Campbell

17. Thierry Henry is the club's record goalscorer in European competitions. How many goals did he score?

    A. 55

    B. 52

    C. 45

    D. 42

18. Who holds the record for the shortest stint as Arsenal manager?

    A. Stewart Houston

    B. Pat Rice

    C. Freddi Ljungberg

    D. Don Howe

19. How many goals did Arsenal concede in the famous Invincibles 2003/04 Premier League Season?

    A. 16

    B. 20

    C. 26

    D. 22

20. In October 2005, Thierry Henry became the Gunners' outright record goalscorer. Who held the title before him?

    A.   Ted Drake

    B.   Ian Wright

    C.   Cliff Bastin

    D.   John Radford

20 Trivia Answers

1. A – Thierry Henry

2. B – Thierry Henry

3. C – Dennis Bergkamp

4. C – 6

5. A – 38

6. C – 27

7. C – 76

8. B – David O'Leary

9. C – David O'Leary

10. C – Ted Drake

11. C – 8

12. A – Ivan Campo

13. D – Cesc Fabregas

14. D – Jock Rutherford

15. B – Cesc Fabregas

16. C – Patrick Viera

17. D – 42

18. B – Pat Rice

19. C – 26

20. B – Ian Wright

10 Fun Facts

1. The Invincibles team of 2003/04 is arguably the greatest team in the history of the Premier League. They were unbeaten through that season, racking up 90 points from 29 wins and 12 draws to win the league. Throughout the Premier League era, other teams may have won more points, had more wins, and drawn fewer games, but none has remained undefeated for an entire season ogf38 games.

2. The honours for the fastest goal in an Arsenal jersey goes to Nicklas Bendtner. In December 2007, he scored against Tottenham Hotspur 1.8 seconds after coming on as a substitute. The Dane went on to be a flamboyant if controversial figure at Arsenal.

3. The club's highest goals scorer is none other than Thierry Henry, with 228 goals in 376 matches. The fleet-footed Frenchman is also number four on the EPL's all-time highest goal scorers list. He is also the Arsenal player with most EPL player of the season (2) and golden boot (4) awards. In April 2021, Henry also became one of the first two Premier League era players to be inducted into the inaugural Premier League Hall of Fame. The other inductee was Alan Shearer.

4. Ted Drake holds the club's record for the most goals in one season (44) and the league alone (42). He set this record in the 1934/35 season. In 1935, he set another record for most goals in a single game, putting 7 goals past Aston Villa.

5. The youngest player to score for Arsenal in a competitive match is Cesc Fabregas. This was in a league cup match against Wolverhampton Wanderers in 2003. Fabregas was just 16 years, 212 days old at the time.

6. At 17 years, 315 days in 1965, John Radford became the youngest player to score a hat trick for Arsenal football club. He played a total of 481 matches across the forward line and scored 149 goals.

7. Central defender, David O'Leary, is the player with the most appearances in the Arsenal jersey. He played for the club from 1975 to 1993, making 722

appearances and scoring 14 goals.

8. Arsenal's highest winning margin in Europe is seven goals. The Gunners accomplished this on two occasions, against Standard Liège (1993 UEFA Cup Winners' Cup) and against Slavia Prague (2007 UEFA Champions League). Both matches ended 7-0 in favor of Arsenal.

9. Emmanuel Petit was the first Arsenal player to start in the final of the World Cup. He achieved the milestone playing for France in the 1998 World Cup against Brazil. Patrick Vieira also came on as a substitute in the match to set up his teammate, Petit, for the third goal in a thumping 3-0 win. Both players would go on to become mainstays in the Premier League for Arsenal for the next few seasons.

10. Thomas Mitchell was the club's first full-time manager between 1897 and 1898. Arsene Wenger holds the record for longest-serving manager as he handled the reins between October 1996 and May 2018. During this period, he held an intense rivalry with Sir Alex Ferguson of Manchester United, and this drove the rivalry between both clubs.

A Short Message from The House of Ballers team

Hello fellow sports fanatic, we hope you enjoyed The Best Arsenal FC Trivia Book Ever.

We'd like to thank you for purchasing and reading it to the end.

We create these books to allow people to, not just expand their knowledge around their favorite clubs and players, but also to keep the passion we all have for the game lit and alive.

Life can come with many challenges and setbacks. But something that never leaves our side is our love for the game.

If you enjoyed reading this book, we'd like to kindly ask for your feedback and thoughts in the review section on Amazon.com.

This will help us continue to make the highest quality books and content for fans all across the world.

>> Scan the QR Code below with your smartphone to leave a short review <<

Ball out,

The House of Ballers Team

Made in United States
North Haven, CT
12 December 2022

28677660R00075